To Our Dear Grandchild

_____

With Love From

_____

Date

_____

Grandparents' Memories

A Keepsake Book

BARBARA BRIGGS MORROW

PUBLICATIONS INTERNATIONAL, LTD.

Barbara Briggs Morrow is a contributing editor for *Midwest Living* magazine and a veteran writer whose work has appeared in *Cosmopolitan* and *Christian Science Monitor*. Her previous books include *American Country Sampler* and *The Gift of Friendship*.

Photo credits:
Cover photo: **N. Schafer/The Stock Market.**

Archive Photos: 28; American Stock: 6; Lambert: 13; **Lisa Brutto:** 11, 32; **Comstock:** 50; **FPG International:** 8, 16, 17, 36; Ruth Bushman: 25; Rob Cage: 67; Ron Chapple: 39, 54; Michael Goldman: 52; Syd Greenberg: 21; Tom Kelley: 41; Mike Malyszko: 60; Michele Salmieri: 57; Mark Scott: 44; Sickles Photo-Reporting: 47; **International Stock:** Scott Barrow: 68; Laurie Bayer: 59; Ken Frick: 34; Roger Markham-Smith: 62; Vesey Vanderburgh: 30; **Suzanne Murphy/Tony Stone Images:** 72; **Planet Art:** Front and back cover border & interior border; **The Stock Market:** George Disario: 70; N. Schafer: Table of contents; **SuperStock:** 4, 19, 24, 48, 64.

Additional photography by **Brian Warling.**

Photo Props: **Lisa Wright.**

Photo Tinting Artist: **Cheryl Winser.**

Flowers provided by **Maria's Flower Boutique, Lincolnwood, IL.**

CONTENTS

BEGINNINGS

For the Record: Grandmother

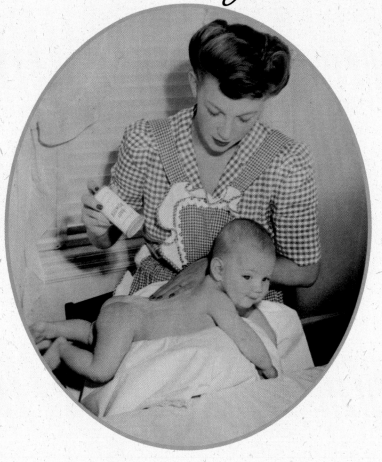

"Mother always said I was a good-size, baby," Grandmother recalled. "Did they weigh you at the hospital?" her granddaughter asked. She was familiar with such procedures now that she had been to the hospital to see her new baby brother. "Well, no. I was born at home." "Did Great Aunt Loretta get to hold you and play with you right after you were born?" the child asked excitedly. Grandma replied gently, "No, sweetie. Babies aren't ready for much playing right away no matter where they're born. Big sisters just have to be patient."

GRANDMOTHER'S BIRTH DATE: _____.

PARENTS' NAMES: _____.

PLACE AND TIME OF BIRTH: _____.

MY BROTHERS, SISTERS, AND OTHER CLOSE FAMILY MEMBERS: _____

_____

_____.

REMEMBERING MY BIRTH, _____ ALWAYS SAID

_____.

AS A BABY, ACCORDING TO THE REST OF THE FAMILY, I WAS _____

_____.

ACCORDING TO THE FAMILY, I SHOWED AN EARLY TALENT FOR _____

_____.

I LOOKED LIKE _____.

THE STORY MOST OFTEN TOLD ABOUT MY EARLY YEARS WAS _____

_____

_____

_____.

Life is a journey, not a destination.

—Anonymous

For the Record: Grandfather

Grandmother produced a sepia-toned photo, slightly ragged at the edges, to prove her point. The picture showed a chubby baby with a heart-shaped face and striking blue eyes, wearing an ornately embroidered linen dress. "You're right, Mom!" the young woman exclaimed. "He did look like Dad as a baby." Then she passed the photo to her five-year-old son, who had been listening quietly. "Look, honey, this is Grandpa."

The child studied the photo with a worried expression. Finally, he announced, "This picture looks like a baby. But it sure doesn't look anything like Grandpa!"

The child is the father of the man.

—William Wordsworth

GRANDFATHER'S BIRTH DATE: _____.

PARENTS' NAMES: _____.

PLACE AND TIME OF BIRTH: _____.

MY BROTHERS, SISTERS, AND OTHER CLOSE FAMILY MEMBERS: _____

_____

_____.

REMEMBERING MY BIRTH, _____ ALWAYS SAID

_____.

AS A BABY, ACCORDING TO THE REST OF THE FAMILY, I WAS _____

_____.

ACCORDING TO THE FAMILY, I SHOWED AN EARLY TALENT FOR _____

_____.

I LOOKED LIKE _____.

THE STORY MOST OFTEN TOLD ABOUT MY EARLY YEARS WAS _____

_____

_____

_____.

Love at First . . .

"Why do you smile at Grandma when she's not even looking?" Michael asked.
"Just remembering," Grandpa replied absently. "Remembering what?" the child insisted.
"Oh . . . a girl with long brown hair and the prettiest eyes you've ever seen."
"Where is that girl, Grandpa?"
"Why, she's right here. Don't you see her?"

I'll never forget the day we met: _____

_____.

What we said to each other: _____

_____.

Our first impressions of each other were _____.

If someone had said then that we would be married, our reaction would have

been _____

_____.

The first evening we spent together was _____

_____.

We knew we were in love when _____

_____.

We were together for _____ before

_____ popped the question.

We celebrated our engagement by _____

_____.

But to see her was to love her,
Love but her, and love for ever.

—*Robert Burns*

9

Happily Ever After

The bride-to-be asked her grandmother how she had handled all the pre-wedding stress—the planning and worrying whether the dresses, the flowers, and a hundred other details would turn out just right. "I'm afraid I can't be much help there," the older woman shrugged. "We were in such a rush to be married. It was as if our lives had been on hold during the war and we couldn't wait to get on with living. There was no thought of waiting for dresses to be made or reserving halls or any of that . . . we just wanted to be together and start a family." The young woman looked thoughtful.

"I don't suppose that makes much sense to you . . ." Grandmother continued.

"It does," was the reply. "It makes me wonder if I'm worrying about the right things."

OUR WEDDING DATE: _____ 19___.

THE BRIDE WORE _____.

THE GROOM WORE _____.

THE BRIDESMAIDS WERE DECKED OUT IN _____.

WHERE WE WERE MARRIED: _____.

MEMORABLE MOMENTS IN THE CEREMONY INCLUDED _____

_____.

There is no more lovely, friendly, and charming relationship,

communion, or company than a good marriage.

—Martin Luther

FAMILY AND FRIENDS WHO ATTENDED: _____

_____

_____

_____.

WE CELEBRATED BY _____

_____.

OF THE GIFTS WE RECEIVED, THE MOST MEANINGFUL WAS _____

_____

_____.

DURING THE FIRST YEARS OF OUR MARRIAGE, WE LIVED _____

_____.

OUR FIRST HOUSE WAS _____. THE FIRST

CAR WE BOUGHT TOGETHER WAS _____.

WE MARKED OUR FIRST ANNIVERSARY BY _____.

A TRADITION WE BEGAN EARLY IN OUR MARRIAGE THAT I WOULD RECOMMEND TO ANY

YOUNG COUPLE STARTING OUT IS _____

_____.

A New Family

"We waited a long time for your dad to come along," Grandpa recalled. "Well, maybe not so long by today's standards. A few years. Then, we were so glad to have him that we used to worry if he slept for more than a couple of hours at a time. Grandma and I would wake him up. Then, almost right away came your Aunt Terry and Uncle Jack." "Did you wake them up, too?" Jessica asked, fascinated at the thought of her dad and aunt and uncle as babies. "No, by then we let everyone sleep just as long as they were willing to," Grandpa replied with a chuckle.

Call it a clan, call it a network, call it a tribe, call it a family.
Whatever you call it, whoever you are, you need one.

—Jane Howard

YOUR (MOM OR DAD) _____ IS OUR _____ CHILD.

BIRTH DATE AND TIME: _____.

BIRTH WEIGHT, LENGTH: _____.

(HE OR SHE) _____ LOOKED LIKE _____.

TO DESCRIBE (HIM OR HER) _____ IN A FEW WORDS AS A BABY:

_____.

YOUR (MOM OR DAD'S) _____ FIRST WORDS WERE:

_____

_____.

FIRST STEPS: _____

_____.

FIRST FRIENDS: _____

_____

_____.

FAVORITE FIRST FOODS: _____

_____.

YOUR AUNTS AND/OR UNCLES AND THEIR BIRTH ORDER:

_____

_____.

Dreams for the Future

More than anything, Maria told her parents over and over, she wanted to dance. Tap, ballet, jazz—she loved them all. She dreamed of the stage, and her parents would play along with her favorite pretend game, "When I'm a famous dancer, I'm going to…" Her mom and dad thought of that dream and smiled as they watched the pretty young teacher climb on to the stage to accept a bouquet of flowers from her excited students. The wide grin and teary eyes showed Maria had enjoyed putting together the junior high musical at least as much as her charges loved performing. After all, she had always dreamed of the stage.

YOUR _____ ALWAYS DREAMED OF

_____ FOR THE FUTURE.

OUR HOPES FOR _____ INCLUDED

_____

_____ .

THE DREAM WE ALL SHARED WAS _____

_____ .

When I approach a child, he inspires in me two sentiments: tenderness

for what he is, and respect for what he may become.

—Louis Pasteur

LOOKING BACK, WE SEE QUALITIES THAT HELPED YOUR _____

_____ BECOME _____.

FOR EXAMPLE:

_____

_____

_____

THEN AND NOW

When I Was a Girl . . .

A blanket of white already covered the ground by noon on Christmas Eve. Outside the bay window, snow continued to fall in swirling sheets. "Do you think it will be canceled, Grandma?" Curtis worried. "We'll just have to see," Grandma replied matter-of-factly, searching for a way to distract the anxious child. "You know," she continued, "when I was your age Christmas services didn't stop because of snow. My father hitched up the sleigh and off we went across the fields. I can still imagine that sleigh—shiny black with red velvet seats." "Didn't you get cold?" the boy asked, wide-eyed. "Oh no!" Grandma answered. "Father tucked a wool blanket around us and we sang Christmas carols all the way to church. I never remember being cold. . . ."

I GREW UP IN _____.

OUR HOUSE OR APARTMENT WAS LOCATED ON _____.

THE DESCRIPTION THAT BEST FITS MY PARENTS IS _____

_____.

MY BEST FRIEND WAS _____.

WE LOVED TO PLAY _____.

MY FAMILY'S FAVORITE MEAL WAS _____.

_____ WAS CONSIDERED A REAL TREAT.

EVENINGS, OUR FAMILY ENJOYED _____.

ONE FEATURE OF MY UPBRINGING THAT I LATER RELIED ON AS AN EXAMPLE IN RAISING MY

OWN FAMILY WAS _____

_____.

Pay attention to the young, and make them just as good as possible.

—Socrates

When I Was a Boy...

"We didn't have uniforms and official teams when I was your age," Grandpa explained patiently. "We would just choose up sides and play."
"But, who told you the rules?" Dean demanded, incredulous. "Oh, we knew how to play," Grandpa replied serenely. "Didn't you have an umpire?" the boy persisted. "No, everybody played fair or they knew they wouldn't get to play again."
"Who kept score?" Dean asked. "Sometimes we didn't," was the reply. "We just played until everyone had to go home or it got dark. It was just for fun."
The boy shook his head, finding such freedom hard to believe.

Ah! Happy Years! once more who would not be a boy?

—George Gordon, Lord Byron

19

THE PLACE WHERE I GREW UP WAS _____.

OUR HOUSE OR APARTMENT WAS _____

_____.

THE DESCRIPTION THAT BEST FITS MY PARENTS IS _____

_____.

MY BEST FRIEND WAS _____.

WE LOVED TO PLAY _____.

MY FAMILY'S FAVORITE MEAL WAS _____.

_____ WAS CONSIDERED A REAL TREAT.

EVENINGS, OUR FAMILY ENJOYED _____.

ONE FEATURE OF MY UPBRINGING THAT I LATER RELIED ON AS AN EXAMPLE IN RAISING MY

OWN FAMILY WAS _____

_____.

Wishes and Dreams

"Why do you watch this race every year, Grandpa?" Caleb asked. "It's exciting. Don't you think so?" Grandpa replied, perched at the edge of his favorite chair for a better view of the cars whizzing around the track. "Not to watch on TV. Maybe if you were there or driving...," the young man's voice trailed off as he imagined taking the wheel of one of the race cars. "Now, you're talking," Grandpa agreed, remembering another boy who thought of little else besides cars and dreamed secretly of racing one day.

I have spread my dreams under your feet.
Tread softly because you tread on my dreams.

—*William Butler Yeats*

YOU MIGHT BE SURPRISED TO KNOW THAT GRANDPA ONCE DREAMED OF _____

_____ .

GRANDMA'S DREAM WAS _____

_____ .

OUR DREAMS THAT CAME TRUE INCLUDE: _____

_____

_____ .

AS A YOUNG MAN, IF GRANDPA WERE GRANTED ONE WISH, IT WOULD HAVE BEEN

_____

_____ .

GRANDMA'S ONE SPECIAL WISH WOULD HAVE BEEN _____

_____ .

THEY SAY "BE CAREFUL WHAT YOU WISH FOR, BECAUSE YOU MIGHT GET IT." THE WISH

THAT FALLS INTO THAT CATEGORY FOR US WAS _____

_____ .

Signs of the Times

"A poodle skirt! That's terrible, Grandma!" little Marika declared indignantly. Grandmother giggled. "Oh, it wasn't made of real poodles. It had a picture of a poodle on it and it swirled around like this when we danced," she said, deftly executing a spin and using a dish towel as a substitute skirt. "Show me how you danced!" the girl begged. "Come on, Granddad, let's show her." Granddad put down his newspaper and rose reluctantly to take Grandma's hand. The couple sashayed happily to an imaginary jitterbug beat, turning and dipping with remembered skill. "I didn't know you two could do that!" Marika exclaimed. The dancers were having too much fun to answer.

We know nothing of tomorrow; our business is to be good and happy today.

—Syndey Smith

WHEN WE WERE KIDS, IF SOMETHING WAS "COOL," WE SAID IT WAS _____

_____.

THE GIRLS ALL WORE _____. THE BOYS DRESSED IN

_____.

THE MUSIC WE LOVED BEST WAS _____. OUR FAVORITE

DANCE WAS _____.

Movies that made a real impression on us were _____

_____.

Our song was _____.

A great evening out included _____

_____.

Some of today's trends that remind us of back then are _____

_____

_____.

Just Between Us

"Once," Grandfather said pointedly, studying the boy who had come home from school empty-handed, "I lost my milk money." "What did you do?" the boy asked. "I wished I could tell my mother someone had taken it away—maybe some of the bigger boys at school. I thought so hard about that story I almost believed it. I told my mother the story and she was so upset that I had been frightened. Then, she said we must go back to school and tell the teacher." "Wow!" the child gasped, "Then what happened?" "I told her the truth. That I was roughhousing with my friends before school, and when it came time for lunch, I couldn't find it. She said she loved me very much, but she wouldn't be able to trust me for awhile. Now," Grandfather continued gently, "do you want to tell me again what happened to your bookbag?"

One of the hardest lessons we learned as children was _____
_____
_____.

If Grandpa ever got into trouble as a child, it was probably over _____
_____
_____.

Grandmother's biggest struggle was _____
_____

An incident that still causes some regret was _____
_____
_____.

The moral of that story is _____
_____
_____.

It is the true nature of mankind to learn from mistakes, not from example.

—Fred Hoyle

In Our Lifetime

No matter what was playing at the theater on the square, every youngster in town lined up for a ticket. If you were lucky, you had enough money left for popcorn and a drink. You walked through musty-smelling curtains into the dark. It was a magic passage to another world where cowboys on horseback galloped to the rescue and where ladies in gauzy dresses and gents in top hats danced and sang instead of simply talking like regular people. We never imagined on those Saturday afternoons that someday we would be able to plug movies into a VCR and watch them whenever we liked. The films are the same—now if someone just could figure out a way to recreate the magic…

SOME OF THE THINGS YOU TAKE FOR GRANTED WERE JUST DREAMS WHEN WE WERE

YOUNG. FOR EXAMPLE: _____

_____

_____

_____.

WHEN WE WERE YOUNG, "FAST" FOOD WAS _____.

OUR MOST "HIGH-TECH" TOY WAS _____.

Necessity is the mother of invention.

—Latin saying

THE HEIGHT OF LUXURY WAS _____

_____ .

THERE WERE NO COMPACT CARS OR MINIVANS. SOME OF THE POPULAR MODELS WERE

_____ .

THEY DIFFERED FROM CARS TODAY IN A NUMBER OF WAYS, SUCH AS _____

_____

_____ .

NOT ALL INVENTIONS WON IMMEDIATE ACCEPTANCE. MANY PEOPLE THOUGHT _____

_____ *WOULD NEVER CATCH ON.*

THE NEW INVENTION WE DREAMED OF OWNING ONE DAY WAS _____

_____ .

THE RECENT INVENTION WE FIND MOST AMAZING IS _____

_____

_____ .

In Perspective

"I want to be a computer programmer or maybe a pilot," Annie blithely announced her ambition of the week. "What did you want to be when you were my age, Grandma?"

"Well . . ." Grandma paused over the pie crust that just didn't seem to want to roll out. "I guess I didn't think about it that way. I knew I would be a wife and a mother."

"But what else?" the girl insisted.

"We thought that was enough," the gray-haired woman replied thoughtfully. "You know how we always tell you that you can be anything you want to be? That wasn't true for girls then, or maybe not for most. We didn't have so many choices."

"It's better now, right?" Annie asked.

"It's better to have choices," Grandma agreed, "but being a mother always will be one of the best ones you can make."

Luck is not chance—
It's toil—
Fortune's expensive smile
Is earned.

—Emily Dickinson

IN MANY WAYS, OPPORTUNITIES FOR ALL PEOPLE HAVE INCREASED IN OUR LIFETIMES.

FOR EXAMPLE, _____

_____

_____.

SOME OF THE MOST POSITIVE CHANGES WE HAVE SEEN INCLUDE _____

_____

_____.

WE'RE PARTICULARLY GLAD YOU LIVE IN A WORLD WHERE _____

_____

_____.

A NICE LONG LETTER IN THE MAILBOX, A LEISURELY TRAIN RIDE—THERE WERE BENEFITS

TO SLOWER-MOVING TIMES THAT WE WISH YOU COULD EXPERIENCE. FOR INSTANCE:

_____

_____

_____.

HOWEVER, NOSTALGIA OVER _____ IS MISGUIDED. THE REAL

STORY IS _____

_____.

Grandmother's Branch

"England! What did they do there?" Annie exclaimed, envisioning knights in shining armor. "Your great, great grandfather was a coal miner," Grandmother explained. "His family was very poor. He knew that here, if he worked hard, he could buy some land." Grandmother nodded toward the fields visible beyond the window. "He bought this land for us." Annie looked out at the land. "Me too?" she asked. "You too," Grandmother said.

The generations of living things pass in a short time, and like
runners hand on the torch of life.

—Lucretius

My family originally came from _____.

They worked as _____.

They came here because of _____

_____.

The earliest ancestor(s) I know about is (are) _____

_____.

Their story is: _____

_____

_____.

I learned what I know about my family tree from _____

_____.

If you want to know more, ask me to show you _____

_____

_____.

Grandfather's Branch

"A real pirate!" Erik was amazed. "That's what they say," Grandfather said, chuckling. "He supposedly was kind of a Robin Hood character, but in the end, the law caught up with him and he was hanged." "Hanged! Wow!" Erik gasped, writing furiously. This school report would be better than he ever dreamed. "I can't wait to tell my teacher." "Hmmm...I'm not so sure.... Let me tell you about your other great, great grandfather. He worked on the railroad...," Grandpa offered, second thoughts setting in. But the boy wasn't listening. "This is so cool. Ted is writing about some old farmers or something..."

MY FAMILY ORIGINALLY CAME FROM _____.

THEY WORKED AS _____.

THEY CAME HERE BECAUSE OF _____

_____.

THE EARLIEST ANCESTOR(S) I KNOW ABOUT IS (ARE) _____

_____

_____.

THEIR STORY IS: _____

_____

_____.

I LEARNED WHAT I KNOW ABOUT MY FAMILY TREE FROM _____

_____.

IF YOU WANT TO KNOW MORE, ASK ME TO SHOW YOU _____

_____

_____.

He that will have his son have respect for him and his orders, must himself

have a great reverence for his son.

—John Locke

Family Stories

I have more memories than if I were a thousand years old.

—Charles Baudelaire

"What if you had to do without electric lights all the time?" Grandpa asked heartily, doing his best to make light of the temporary power outage.

The girls shrugged, the candle burning in the center of the kitchen table showing quivering lips and teary eyes. Grandpa plunged on, "My grandfather got mad at the electric company before I was even born, and he had the power turned off—never allowed it to be turned back on. Some people thought he was just a character, but I always admired him. He said the power company just plain charged too much money."

"What did you do?" the older girl asked. "Well, when I visited there we used candles just like this one. Water came from a pump out back. I was the youngest so I had to fetch it—bucket after bucket," Grandpa recalled. The girls giggled at the thought of their grandpa working so hard, momentarily forgetting the surrounding darkness. "Maybe I'll tell them not to turn the power back on," Grandpa suggested, eyes twinkling. "Nooo, Grandpa!" the girls squealed.

OUR FAMILY HAS HAD ITS SHARE OF INTERESTING CHARACTERS, SUCH AS _____

_____

_____

_____.

A family story you may not have heard yet is _____

_____

_____

_____

_____.

Every family has a skeleton or two in the closet; I guess you could say

ours is _____

_____

_____

_____.

The ancestor who is most admired is _____.

That's because _____

_____

_____

_____.

Traits and Ties

In the annual portrait, among his dark-haired, dark-eyed siblings, the fair-skinned, tow-headed boy looked as if he had been grouped accidentally with the wrong family. "I don't look like anyone, Grandma," Adam wailed. "Oh, yes you do. A handsome man who lived a long time ago," Grandma soothed. "Would you like to see his picture?"
Finding the sepia-toned print took some digging through the old cedar chest. "See, this was my great grandfather," Grandma sighed. "I never knew him, but everyone talked about what a handsome, charming fellow he was, and so strong—just like you with all your sports." The boy studied the the man's fine features and his engaging smile.
"Will I look like that?" he wondered. "I wouldn't be a bit surprised," Grandma said.

CERTAIN PHYSICAL TRAITS RUN IN OUR FAMILIES. _____

_____ IS (ARE) COMMON ON GRANDPA'S SIDE.

IN GRANDMA'S FAMILY, _____

_____ HAVE (HAS) BEEN PASSED FROM GENERATION TO GENERATION.

THERE ALSO ARE SOME FAMILY PERSONALITY TRAITS, SUCH AS _____

_____

_____.

IN LOOKS, YOU FAVOR _____

_____

_____.

PLACE OLD FAMILY
PHOTO HERE

IN YOUR PERSONALITY, WE SEE SOMETHING OF _____

_____

_____.

It is the common wonder of all men, how among so many millions
of faces, there should be none alike.

—*Thomas Browne*

FAMILY SNAPSHOTS

For the Record: Our Child

The photo showed a young woman sitting up in a hospital bed cradling what looked at first glance like a bundle of blankets. Closer inspection showed a tiny face. The woman looked worried. Grandma pointed to the sleeping infant. "That's your Dad and that's me." "Why do you look so serious, Grandma?" Sean wondered. "Oh, Grandpa just caught me off guard in this one. Having a baby's a big responsibility, and we thought about all the things to come," Grandma answered. "Everything? Did you think about me, Grandma?" "No, little one," she said pulling the little boy onto to her lap. "If I had, I would have been smiling for sure."

YOUR _____'s BIRTH DATE IS _____.

PLACE AND TIME OF BIRTH: _____.

WEIGHT AND LENGTH: _____.

OUR FIRST THOUGHTS UPON SEEING THE BABY WERE _____

_____.

THE FIRST THING OUR PARENTS SAID WHEN THEY SAW OUR BABY WAS _____

_____.

SOME DETAILS OF THAT DAY YOU MAY NOT HAVE HEARD BEFORE: _____

_____

_____

_____

AS AN INFANT, WE AGREED THAT YOUR _____ LOOKED LIKE

_____.

AS A BABY, _____'s TEMPERAMENT COULD ONLY

BE DESCRIBED AS _____.

There's only one pretty child in the world, and every mother has it.

—*Proverb*

Toddling Times

"I'll bet that little one is walking well before she's a year old. You know, walking early runs in the family," Grandma predicted, proudly watching her first grandchild struggling to stand in her crib. "Oh Mom! You don't think you're just a little bit predjudiced," the child's mother laughed. "Is that so?" was the tart response. "You weren't much older than this when you were walking all over the place. You were so tiny you could walk right underneath the kitchen table without bumping your head."

"You better tell me everything else amazing that I did so I can be prepared," the young mother replied, only half joking.

FOR THE RECORD, HERE ARE A FEW OF YOUR _____ 'S FIRSTS:

FIRST FOODS: _____

_____.

FIRST STEPS: _____

_____.

FIRST WORDS: _____

_____.

Parents learn a lot from their children about coping with life.

—Muriel Spark

It took dedicated parents to understand some of those first words. Some "toddlerisms" that made us smile were: _____

_____

_____.

Your _____'s favorite game was _____.

The biggest struggles we had with our toddler were over _____

_____.

The toy your_____

loved best was _____

_____.

During those toddler years, _____

showed an early talent for _____

_____.

At the same time, we wondered if your _____

_____ would ever _____

_____

PLACE PHOTO HERE:
YOUR CHILD AS
A TODDLER

School Days

"You think this is hard? When your dad was in school, he had to do these problems without a calculator. Have you ever tried to use a slide rule?" Grandpa asked.

"That was the Dark Ages," Marcus snorted, unimpressed.

"I thought I was the one who grew up in the Dark Ages," Grandpa teased.

"No, you grew up in the Dark Dark Ages," the boy teased back. "Now could you please help me figure out these math problems?"

YOUR _____ 'S FIRST SCHOOL WAS _____.

_____ ALSO ATTENDED _____

_____.

YOUR _____ HAD A REAL RAPPORT WITH

_____ , A TEACHER AT _____.

_____ 'S BEST SUBJECTS WERE _____

_____.

_____ WAS NEVER A FAVORITE.

_____ 'S GREATEST TRIUMPH AT SCHOOL WAS PROBABLY

_____.

THE SCHOOL YEARS YOUR _____ SEEMED TO ENJOY

THE MOST WERE _____.

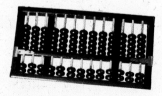

There is only one sound method or moral education.
It is in teaching people to think.

—*Everett Dean Martin*

Telling Tales

The young man reluctantly produced a crumpled sheet of pink paper. "So this is what the surprise visit is about?" Grandpa said, studying the paper. "Going 45 in a 35 zone, huh? Not the worst it could be, but bad enough. Have you told your dad?" "I can't, Grandpa. I just wasn't paying attention for minute. I don't know where that cop came from. Dad will never understand," the young man moaned. "Oh, I don't know about that," the older man said. "Seems I've heard a story like this somewhere before . . ." "You mean MY dad got a ticket?" the young man asked hopefully, face brightening. "Let's just say everyone makes mistakes, and your dad is a wise man who understands that," Grandpa said, patting the young man on the back. "Now, go home and confess!"

To confess a fault freely is the next thing to being innocent of it.

—Publilius Syrus

As a child, your _____ got into trouble more than

once because of _____.

The lesson finally was learned when _____

_____.

In our house, _____ was the disciplinarian.

Your _____ would say

_____ was the softie.

Some youngsters are angels and some are little devils. Your _____

_____ fell into the _____ category.

The teenage scrape we laughed about later was _____

_____.

One lesson you could learn from the story is _____

_____.

Milestones

"Thought you might want to stay in your Mom's old room," Grandpa said. As Monica set down her suitcase, a line of trophies and certificates on the bookshelf caught her eye. "Are all those Mom's?" she asked. "There's cheerleading and debate. What's that small one for?"

"Sometimes, I think that one made me proudest of all," Grandpa replied. "One year she decided to go out for track. She went to every practice and did everything the coach said, but she never won a race. That was for being the most improved member of the team."

"Why would you be proud of that, Grandpa? She won all these other things," the girl asked. "Because she stuck with it even though she lost over and over," said the still-proud father. "That's a lot tougher than winning."

In the long run men hit only what they aim at. Therefore, though they should fail immediately, they had better aim at something high.

—Henry David Thoreau

YOUR _____ GAVE US MANY WONDERFUL MOMENTS.

SOME OF OUR PROUDEST WERE: _____

_____

_____.

IN SCHOOL, YOUR _____'S

ACCOMPLISHMENTS INCLUDED _____

_____

_____.

PLACE PHOTO HERE:
YOUR CHILD'S SPECIAL
ACCOMPLISHMENT

IN OTHER AREAS OF LIFE, RECOGNITION CAME BECAUSE OF____

_____.

SOME OF THOSE HONORS INCLUDED _____

_____.

THESE DAYS, YOUR _____ DOESN'T TAKE ENOUGH CREDIT

SOMETIMES. FOR EXAMPLE, DID YOU KNOW _____

_____

_____.

Another New Family

Her parents remembered noticing no extra spark between their daughter and their son-in-law-to-be or feeling that this young man might be the one. They liked the young man, but hadn't noticed any special difference with him. Lacking this sort of sign, the young couple's decision to marry seemed sudden. Their daughter set them straight on that score. "You're not supposed to know he's the one until I tell you," she laughed. "You don't fall in love with him, I do. It's all right if YOU have to learn to love him."

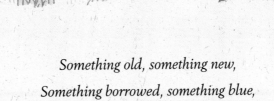

Something old, something new,
Something borrowed, something blue,
And a lucky sixpence in her shoe.

—*Wedding rhyme*

WE KNEW YOUR PARENTS WOULD BE MARRIED WHEN _____

_____.

TO US, THEIR COURTSHIP SEEMED _____.

THEY SEEMED LIKE A _____ MATCH, BECAUSE

_____.

THEIR WEDDING COULD ONLY BE DESCRIBED AS _____

_____.

THE MOST MEMORABLE PART OF THE CEREMONY WAS _____

_____.

AFTERWARD, THEY CELEBRATED BY _____

_____.

Then There Was You

"A grandmother! That's not possible, you're much too young," Martha exclaimed,
studying her friend's trim figure and dark hair cut in a carefree bob. "Of course I'm old
enough, and I'm ready!" Amy declared. "I pulled out all the old toys and books,
and I've dusted off the old crib for when they come to visit. I can't wait."
"But your daughter's only...," Martha stammered. "The same age as yours," Amy offered.
"That means...," Martha pondered, shocked. "I'm the same age as you," Amy obligingly
finished the sentence. "Maybe if you're lucky, you'll be a grandmother soon, too."

PLACE PHOTO HERE: YOUR GRANDCHILD AS A NEWBORN

WHEN WE HEARD YOU WERE ON THE WAY, WE FELT _____

_____.

WE FOUND OUT WHEN _____.

BEING GRANDPARENTS SOUNDED LIKE A _____

_____ JOB TO US.

WE DID OFFER YOUR PARENTS-TO-BE A FEW PIECES OF

ADVICE, SUCH AS _____

_____

_____

_____.

WAITING FOR YOU, YOUR PARENTS SEEMED _____

_____.

WE HELPED PREPARE FOR YOUR ARRIVAL BY _____

_____.

Let us have love and more love.

—Abdul Baha

The Day You Were Born...

"It's time," the woman hung up the phone with a look of surprise. "It's time?" her husband asked excitedly, jumping up from his favorite chair. "Well, what do we do?" The couple looked at each other, puzzled. "Well, I guess there's not much we can do, except wait," the woman said. "I'll put the coffee on."

"Everyone says having grandchildren is so darn easy," the grandfather-to-be complained. "This is harder than when we had our own."

WE HEARD THAT IT WAS TIME FOR YOUR ARRIVAL FROM _____

_____.

THE WAIT WAS _____.

WE PASSED THE TIME BY _____.

THE DAY YOU WERE BORN, WE _____

_____

Every child comes with the message that God is not yet discouraged of man.

—Rabindranath Tagore

We saw you for the first time when _____.

Our reaction was _____.

We thought you looked like _____.

The first time she held you, Grandma thought _____

_____.

When Grandpa held you, he _____

_____.

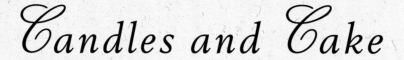

Candles and Cake

The toddler gleefully tore the paper from the big box and smiled at his grandparents as if to say, "Thanks, I really like this great paper. You couldn't have given me a birthday gift I liked more." Then, paper in hand, he happily trotted away, hoping one of the adults would chase him. "Grandpa, you open the box for him," Grandma urged.

"What have you two done?" their son demanded, surveying the contents. "A bike? He won't be ready for that for awhile." Grandpa returned, "It's one of those little ones. He'll be peddling around in no time. What's the matter?"

"Well," the son admitted grudgingly. "I got him one, too."

FOR YOUR FIRST BIRTHDAY, OUR GIFT WAS _____.

YOUR REACTION WAS _____.

YOUR FIRST BIRTHDAY PARTY THAT WE ATTENDED WAS _____

_____.

YOUR FAVORITE PART OF THE FESTIVITIES SEEMED TO BE _____.

THE GIFT WE HAD THE MOST FUN BUYING FOR YOU WAS _____

_____.

THE GIFT WE HOPE YOU'LL ALWAYS KEEP IS _____

_____.

58

One cannot have too large a party.

—Jane Austen

Holiday Memories

"I should be helping you more, Mom," Julie insisted, as she shifted to feed the baby one-handed so she could use the other to scrub dip from the cranky three-year-old's face. Basting the turkey and checking the progress of the potatoes boiling on the stove, her mother laughed. "You have your hands full. Just think of these holiday meals as part of my gift to you. Now, let me hold that baby."

"Well, okay, but what's my gift to you?" Taking the smiling baby in her arms, the woman looked at her daughter with mock surprise. "You have to ask?"

Ring out the old, ring in the new,

Ring, happy bells, across the snow:

The year is going, let him go;

Ring out the false, ring in the true.

—*Lord Alfred Tennyson,* In Memoriam

ALL THE HOLIDAYS SPENT WITH YOU ARE PRECIOUS, BUT OUR FAVORITE IS _____

_____ .

THE HOLIDAY TRADITION THAT IS ESPECIALLY IMPORTANT TO US IS _____

_____ .

WE HOPE YOU'LL CONTINUE THAT TRADITION BECAUSE _____

_____ .

ONE HOLIDAY INCIDENT INVOLVING YOU THAT WE'LL ALWAYS REMEMBER IS _____

_____

_____

_____ .

THERE WAS ONE GIFT WE GAVE YOU THAT WE PROBABLY WERE MORE EXCITED ABOUT

THAN YOU WERE. THAT'S BECAUSE _____

_____ .

WE LOVE ALL YOUR GIFTS, BUT ONE THAT WAS ESPECIALLY MEANINGFUL WAS _____

_____ .

Proud Moments

The orchestra played well, but the couple had eyes for only one performer—their granddaughter. They imagined they could hear the fine, clear strains of her violin above those of the other instruments. Afterward, the girl was surprised and a little embarrassed to see them waiting. "You guys didn't have to drive all the way here for this concert. It's not even the biggest one of the year." "Everything you're part of is a big deal to us, honey," Grandpa reassured her. "You were wonderful."

The girl started to protest, remembering missed notes and places where the whole orchestra had faltered, but looking into their eyes, she could see her grandparents meant every word they had said. "It's great to have fans," she said simply, taking their arms. "So how about taking the big star out for ice cream?"

If music be the food of love, play on.

—*Shakespeare*, The Merchant of Venice

We're always proud of you. Some of the events we've been particularly

pleased to be part of include _____

_____.

It isn't just what you do that makes us proud; it's who you are. Some of your

qualities that we especially admire are _____

_____.

One of the first times you made us bust our buttons was _____

_____

_____.

We're guilty of bragging about you at times. Here's what we say: _____

_____

_____.

Events that we're looking forward to being part of in your life include

_____

_____.

Adventures Together

"Grandpa, can we go back to the hotel and swim?" the two boys begged. "What's the matter with you guys? We haven't done all the rides yet!" Grandpa demanded in mock disappointment. "I want go on Space Mountain again!"

"Well, what if we do that tomorrow?" the older boy asked seriously, taking a tone he had heard his parents use. "Well, I guess so. Do you promise?" Grandpa wheedled.

"We'll see," the boy replied sternly.

Oh, the wild joys of living!

—Robert Browning

ONE OF OUR FAVORITE WAYS TO SPEND TIME WITH YOU IS _____

_____ .

ONE EXCURSION WE'LL ALWAYS REMEMBER IS _____

_____

_____ .

YOU WORE US OUT THE TIME WE _____

_____ .

ANOTHER TIME, WE WORE YOU OUT. REMEMBER WHEN _____

_____ .

SOME OF THE ADVENTURES WE HOPE TO SHARE WITH YOU IN THE FUTURE INCLUDE

_____

_____

_____ .

A LEGACY

Across Generations

Shock was Carrie's first reaction. Her own children! How could they? What would people say? How could they embarass her this way? Suddenly, questions racing through her mind carried her back to the past. She was a young woman again sitting on the porch swing with her grandmother, sobbing over her parents' disapproval. "How can they think that?" she had wailed. "Why don't they understand?"

"Things look different from your parents' point of view," Grandmother had said quietly. "Well, why don't you see things that way?" she had asked. "Maybe I do," the older woman had answered. "But I also care about you. Over the years, I've learned that letting someone know that is more important than telling them what I think."

THE PIECE OF ADVICE THAT HAS SERVED US WELL TIME AND AGAIN IS _____

_____

_____ .

_____ GETS CREDIT FOR THAT BIT OF WISDOM. IT WAS

PASSED ALONG WHEN _____

_____ .

YEARS AGO, WHEN _____ SAID _____

_____

_____ , WE SHOULD HAVE LISTENED.

The heart of the old is always young in two things: in love
for the world and length of hope.

—Mohammed

ON THE OTHER HAND, THE ADVICE THAT SHOULD HAVE BEEN IGNORED WAS _____

_____

_____

_____.

Life's Lessons

"I don't have time for anything like that," Will declared. "I'm anxious to get out there after graduation and make some money. Sure this fellowship would give me a chance to see Europe, but there's lots of time for that, Gramps." The older man weighed this speech, knowing his grandson expected him to come down solidly in favor of taking a job immediately. Hadn't that been the kind of life he himself had led?

"I'm sorry to say this, but you're wrong," he said finally. The young man looked shocked. "There isn't plenty of time to do everything you want to do," Grandfather continued. "Get the extra credentials, see Europe. Work—now that's what there's plenty of time for, and it will wait. This opportunity won't."

ONE LESSON LIFE HAS TAUGHT US IS _____

_____.

ON THE SUBJECT OF LOVE AND MARRIAGE, WE'VE COME TO BELIEVE _____

_____.

IN REGARD TO MONEY AND FINANCES, WE'VE LEARNED THAT A GOOD RULE TO LIVE BY IS

_____

_____.

LOOKING AT YOUR GENERATION, ONE WAY YOU SEEM TO BE MISSING THE BOAT IS _____

_____.

ON THE OTHER HAND, YOU SEEM A LOT SMARTER THAN WHEN WE WERE AT YOUR AGE

ABOUT _____

_____.

The greatest good is wisdom.

—*St. Augustine*, Soliloquies

Memories to Cherish

The man breathed in the aroma of the freshly cut wood, wondering if that wasn't what he loved most about his workshop. Then he realized he was thinking of his grandfather. He saw the big calloused hands, gnarled and knotty at the joints, carefully planing a piece of walnut. The old man had worked slowly and explained every step to the little boy who watched. "Always patient. Never too busy for me," the man thought, as he laid out tools for that afternoon's project. He and his granddaughter would finish that birdhouse today.

The heart that loves is always young.

—Greek proverb

ONE MEMORY OF OUR TIME TOGETHER THAT WE HOPE YOU'LL ALWAYS CHERISH IS _____

_____

_____.

THE MEMORY OF YOU THAT WE'LL ALWAYS HOLD DEAR IS _____

_____

_____.

IF THERE WERE ONLY ONE THING WE COULD TEACH YOU, IT WOULD BE _____

_____

_____.

YOU MAY NOT REALIZE IT, BUT SOMETHING YOU HAVE TAUGHT US IS_____

_____

_____.

THE CHARACTER TRAITS WE HOPE YOU WILL REMEMBER AND CARRY THROUGHOUT YOUR

LIFE ARE: _____

_____

_____.

Dreams to Live

"Mom says she wants me to think about medicine and Dad says an MBA is the way to go. What do you want me to do, Grandma?" the frustrated boy asked. "I want you to be happy and I want you to be the best person you can be," Grandma replied without hesitation. "Oh, everyone says that. It doesn't help," the youth wailed. "How do I do it?" "Only you can figure that out," Grandma said firmly. "And I suspect you won't until you stop worrying about what everyone else thinks and start thinking for yourself."

Hitch your wagon to a star.

—Ralph Waldo Emerson

OUR DREAM FOR YOU IS _____

_____.

FROM OUR POINT OF VIEW, IT SEEMS THE BEST WAY TO ACHIEVE THAT IS _____

_____

_____.

IN DIFFICULT TIMES, WE HOPE YOU WILL REMEMBER _____

_____.

SOMETIMES, YOUR LIFE TURNS OUT VERY DIFFERENTLY FROM WHAT YOU DREAMED. OUR

ADVICE TO YOU IF THAT HAPPENS IN YOUR LIFE IS _____

_____

_____.

WHEN YOU THINK OF US WE HOPE YOU WILL REMEMBER _____

_____.

WHEREVER YOUR LIFE AND YOUR DREAMS TAKE YOU, ALWAYS REMEMBER THAT WE LOVE

YOU, FOREVER.

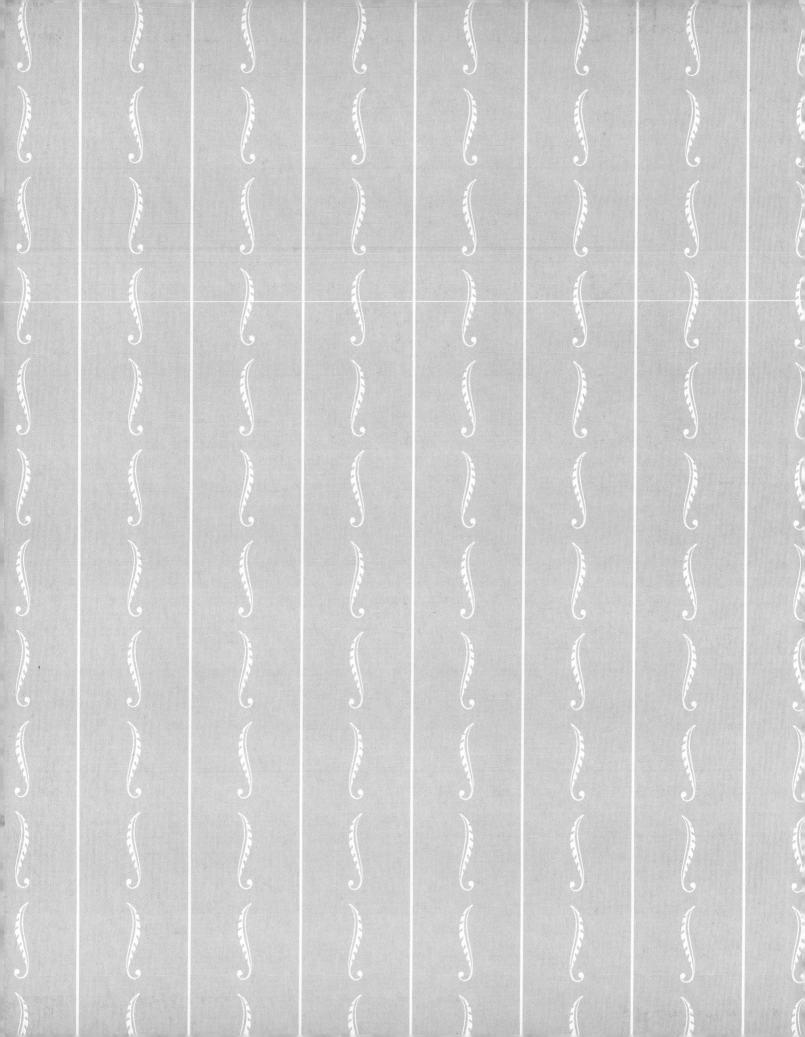